THE
CLOZE
LINE

Blackline Masters for
Comprehension Development

Robin Jones-Elgar

High Noon Books
Novato, California

High Noon Books
20 Commercial Blvd.
Novato, CA 94949-6191

International Standard Book Number: 0-87879-864-1

6 5 4 3 2 1 0 9 8 7
3 2 1 0 9 8 7 6 5 4

DIRECTIONS

This activity book of nearly sixty worksheets is available to you to photocopy for your students as long as copies are not sold to students. It was designed and planned for upper elementary and middle school students, and for slow students in special classes at the secondary level.

Research has shown that one of the best routes available to teachers for developing both decoding skills and comprehension is the regular use of cloze activity sheets. This program was field tested with a variety of youngsters from 6th through the 10th grades and found to be successful in achieving both goals.

Each worksheet, except for the last four (see below) includes a set of Key Words, a short paragraph, and anywhere from three to six questions. In addition, there are two practice sheets, #A and #B, following these directions, should it be necessary to introduce the concept of clozure to your students.

This blackline activity book is organized into these groupings:

Activites 1-10	Each of these worksheets offers in the Key Words section eight words to be written in eight spaces in the paragraph story, followed by three to four comprehension/recall questions. The Key Words are presented in their order of insertion into the paragraph.
Activities 11-30	Each of these worksheets offers eight words to be inserted in eight spaces in the paragraph story followed by three to four questions. The words, however, are not in the order of their insertion.
Activities 31-40	Each of these worksheets offers ten words, eight of which are to be inserted in eight spaces in the paragraph story followed by six questions. The words are not in the order of their insertion.
Activities 41-50	Each of these worksheets offers twelve words, eight of which are to be inserted in the paragraph story which follows. These stories are followed by six questions. The words are not in the order of their insertion.
Activities 51-54	These are one page selections which offer no key words to work from. The student must use his/her understanding of the material and write in an appropriate word that holds the story together. For teacher use, suggested completions are given for each of these selections. Even though student responses may vary, accept insertions if they meet the criterion of sensible judgment.

Each worksheet is numbered so that you can keep an accurate record of which worksheets your students have attempted. While you certainly may skip around the book, it is recommended that you try, as much as possible, to distribute worksheets sequentially. For example, if your students successfully handle the practice sheets, then see how well they function with a few worksheets from the 1-10 group. If, after a few worksheets they are performing adequately, move on to the 11-30 group.

If you have a selection available of different colored photocopy papers, then you might, for record keeping, copy the first ten, for example, on yellow paper, and the next twenty on blue paper, and so on. Experiment with these sheets. Perhaps it will be necessary to introduce the Key Words on the chalkboard and orally and then have your students use them in sentences, with a definition, possibly, for each word. Confusion in writing the correct word in the correct space might be the result of a poor understanding of the word!

If the students can properly pronounce the word and even insert each one into its correct space, but have difficulty with the comprehension check, then ask them to orally read the completed story paragraph to see if it "makes sense" to them.

When your students have completed each worksheet, turn the correction process into a group learning activity. Maybe you will want students to exchange their papers. Maybe not. But there is so much to be learned when students correct either their own or someone else's paper.

Remember. This is a learning activity. It is well accepted that quite often slow learners learn more efficiently when the learning is more incidental than direct. Therefore, keep it an engaging learning situation.

Good luck!

Practice Page 1

Write the word that fits in each space.

1. I like it when it is nice and _____ .

   cat   sunny   ocean

2. I always try to be a good _____ to my friends.

   building   doctor   friend

3. Some people think that the _____ is man's best friend.

   hair   tree   dog

4. Who has the _____ to my car?

   engine   desk   keys

5. Have you ever seen such a tall _____ ?

   sky   snow   building

6. Who took the cookie from the _____ jar?

   face   yesterday   cookie

7. Have you ever traveled on an _____ ?

   ski   car   airplane

8. Please bring me the book with the yellow _____ .

   dog   monster   cover

9. Some day I would like to have my very own _____ .

   zero   happy   convertible

10. I'd like to have a parttime _____ .

    car   job   never

Practice Page 2

Write the word that fits in each space.

1. Get the hammer on the _____ and bring it to _____ .

   zoo   fly   table   ask   me

2. I'll see you at _____ . Be ready to _____ .

   afternoon   7:00 p.m.   airplane   go   next

3. The journey of a _____ miles begins with the _____ step.

   China   first   night   flower   thousand

4. We see with the _____ but we hear with the _____ .

   nose   ears   mouth   lips   eyes

5. It's _____ today. Please get me some _____ water.

   find   highway   hot   ice   head

6. I don't know what _____ it is. My _____ stopped.

   oven   never   watch   idea   time

7. I didn't have a _____ yesterday. That's why I got so wet when it _____ .

   house   believe   rained   can   raincoat

8. You will _____ him. Just follow his _____ .

   tall   look   footsteps   fish   find

9. I really liked going to the _____ last weekend. But the water seemed too _____ .

   circus   beach   ski   light   salty

10. Tom likes to _____ in the mountains. He feels _____ when he gets back home.

    piano   never   camp   picnic   great

Name_____ Date_____

┌─ KEY WORDS ──────────────────────────────────────┐

　　spending　　　　after　　　　days　　　　idea

　　father　　　both　　　newspaper　　hamburgers

└──┘

After School Job

Bob wanted to earn some _____ money. He thought that if he got

a job _____ school he could work a few _____ a

week. He talked the _____ over with his _____

and with his teacher. They _____ liked the idea. Bob looked through

the _____ . He got a job selling _____ .

He liked the job and he earned $20 a week.

Bob wanted to earn some
_____ money for his car.
_____ spending money.
_____ money for clothes.

He talked with
_____ his teacher and good friend Bill.
_____ his music teacher and his dad.
_____ his teacher and his dad.

He found a job selling
_____ used cars.
_____ hamburgers.
_____ newspapers.

Name_____ Date_____

┌─ KEY WORDS ──────────────────────────────┐

decorate	idea	job	school
Saturday	dance	night	terrific

└──┘

The School Dance

Ellen and Betty wanted to help at the big school dance. Jim asked them if they would help _____ the school auditorium. They thought that was a great _____ . It was a big _____ so they asked Bill and Ed to help. They all met at _____ on _____ morning. The _____ was being held that _____ . Everyone thought the auditorium looked _____ when the dance started.

Ellen and Betty asked

_____ Jim to help them.

_____ Bill and Ed to help them.

_____ Bill and Jim to help them.

They wanted to fix the school auditorium for the big

_____ football game.

_____ school party.

_____ school dance.

Everyone thought the auditorium looked terrific

_____ after the dance.

_____ during the dance.

_____ when the dance started.

Name_____ Date_____

KEY WORDS

students	game	star	sick
champion	league	counting	well

The Football Game

It was football day at Lake High School. All the _____ wanted their team to win the _____ against Snow High School. Buck Freeman was the _____ player at Lake High. But Buck had been _____ for two weeks. If Lake won this game, it would be the _____ team in the _____ . Everyone was _____ on Buck. Was he _____ enough to play?

What day was it at Lake High School?
_____ Saturday
_____ basketball day
_____ football day

Who was the star football player for Lake High School?
_____ Buck Evans
_____ Buck Wilson
_____ Buck Freeman

Lake was going to play against
_____ Wilson High School
_____ Snow High School
_____ Mountain High School

Name_____ Date_____

┌─ KEY WORDS ─────────────────────────────┐
| picnic   day   idea   potato |
| sandwiches   drinks   chips   rain |
└──┘

Title ? ? ?

Kate and Nora decided to ask Jill and Sandra to go on a _____
with them. They thought they could go up to Long Lake for the _____ .
Jill and Sandra thought it was a great _____ . Jill said she would fix the
_____ salad. Sandra said she would fix _____ .
Kate and Nora said they would bring soft _____ and potato
_____ . Everything went well except that when they were ready
to leave it started to _____ .

What would you name this story?
_____ The Picnic
_____ Rained Out
_____ .

Who said she would fix the sandwiches?
_____ Jill
_____ Nora
_____ Sandra

Where did they think would be a good place for the picnic?
_____ Lizard Valley
_____ Emerald Lake
_____ Long Lake

Name_____ Date_____

The School Play

Mrs. Marker put a sign up on the school _____ board. It was right in the main school _____ . This is what it said:

> We need students who like to _____ . We are going to have a
> school _____ . Come and sign up. Everyone is welcome.
>
> Mrs. Marker

Judy and Ed decided it could be a lot of _____ to try out for the play. The _____ day they went to see Mrs. Marker. There was a long _____ of students in front of her _____ . When they finally got in to see her, she said, "I'm sorry. All the parts have been taken. Try next time."

Mrs. Marker put this on the school bulletin board

_____ a flower

_____ a note about vacations

_____ a sign about the school play

The two students who decided to sign up for the play were

_____ Mark and Ed.

_____ Jack and Jill.

_____ Judy and Ed.

Mrs. Marker wanted

_____ only tall students to sign up.

_____ students who liked to act to sign up.

_____ just girls to sign up.

Name_____ Date_____

┌─ KEY WORDS ────────────────────────────────────┐
| money   car   expensive   used |
| insurance   monthly   years   condition |
└──┘

The Used Car

Jim had worked hard and saved a lot of _____ . He decided that it
was time to buy a new _____ for himself. But when he looked around,
they were all too _____ . So he decided that he would
buy a _____ car. He had to make sure that he could pay for the
_____ and that he could earn enough to make the
_____ payments. It took a month but he found a car ten
_____ old in good _____ . That little used car
became his first car.

Jim had saved a lot of money by
_____ baby sitting.
_____ gardening jobs.
_____ working hard.

At first, Jim wanted to buy a
_____ new car.
_____ small truck.
_____ used car.

Before he bought anything, he had to make sure that he could
_____ pay for the insurance.
_____ pay for the monthly payments.
_____ pay for both of the above.
_____ pay for his medical bills.

Name_____ Date_____

country	Sunday	pony	limping
looked	house	thanked	Bert

The Injured Pony

The Smith family — Dad, Mom, Bert, and Sarah — was taking a Sunday ride in the _____ . It was a nice sunny _____ . They passed a lot of small farms. As they passed one small _____ , Bert saw it _____ .

"Dad, stop the car," Bert yelled out. Dad stopped the car. They all _____ at the pony. "That pony is injured," Sara said. "We have to tell someone," Bert said.

Dad drove his car to the nearest small _____ . A man came to the door when Dad knocked on it. Dad told him about the injured pony. The man _____ Dad and _____ for letting him know.

The Smith family was taking a drive
_____ to the mountains to go skiing.
_____ in the country.
_____ to the beach.

Bert saw
_____ a pony with a red saddle.
_____ a pony limping.
_____ a pony with two children riding it.

When Dad told the man at the nearest house, the man
_____ was angry at Dad and Bert.
_____ was happy about the news.
_____ thanked Dad and Bert for telling him.

Name_____ Date_____

```
┌─ KEY WORDS ─────────────────────────────────────┐
│     homes        food        car       smoke     │
│     fire         stop        woods     can       │
└──────────────────────────────────────────────────┘
```

Fire in the Woods

Mark, Don, and Jim decided they would like to go camping in the woods that were near their _____ . They got their sleeping bags and _____ to take along with them. They put it all in Mark's _____ .

As they got closer to the woods, Don said, "I smell _____ . Do you think there is a _____ here?" Don was right.

A forest ranger told them to _____ the car. "What's wrong?" Mark asked.

The forest ranger said, "There is a big fire in the _____ . We aren't letting anyone in until it is under control."

"Can we help fight the fire?" Jim asked.

"The forest ranger answered, "You sure _____ . Park over there and come with me."

Mark, Don, and Jim decided they would like to
_____ camp out in the woods near their homes.
_____ camp out at the beach because it was good weather.
_____ help clean up the school grounds.

The boys did not know there was a fire until
_____ Don's mother called them on the telephone.
_____ they saw animals running out of the woods.
_____ a forest ranger told them.

When the forest ranger told them about the fire they decided to
_____ go right back home.
_____ stay and help fight the fire.
_____ camp in the woods anyway.

Name_____ Date_____

┌─ KEY WORDS ─────────────────────────────────────┐
| |
| passing   duck   believe   nature |
| call   climate   lake   correct |
| |
└──┘

The Lonely Duck

Ellen was taking a walk near her home. She was _____ a small lake when she heard what sounded like a _____ . She could hardly _____ it because wild ducks never had stopped before near her small town. But when she got to the lake, she saw a duck swimming around. When she got home, she called the _____ museum and described the duck. The man at the museum thanked her for her _____ and said that it was strange. He said that this kind of duck was traveling to a warmer _____ and probably got mixed up. He said he would go to the _____ and try to get the duck back on its _____ course.

Ellen was taking a walk near

_____ the center of her small town.

_____ her home.

_____ the tall mountains.

She was surprised when she heard the sound of

_____ an elephant.

_____ a duck.

_____ a quail.

The man at the museum told her that the duck was probably

_____ in town to visit other ducks.

_____ off course on its way to a warmer climate.

_____ sick and needed medical help.

Name_____ Date_____

KEY WORDS

repair	people	things	afford
time	cafeteria	meeting	Bill

School Lunch Meeting

Edna wanted to have a meeting of the students at Washington High School who liked to _____ things. Even Bill agreed there were a lot of _____ in town who had broken _____ but could not _____ to have them repaired. Mr. Masters, the school principal, said that the only _____ they could meet was at lunch time. He said he would let them use the school _____ . When they finally had the school lunch _____ , eighty-three students showed up. When that happened, Edna and _____ knew that they would be able to help a lot of people.

Edna wanted to have a meeting of students who
_____ liked to paint houses.
_____ wanted to help the sick people in town.
_____ liked to repair broken things.

Mr. Masters, the school principal, said the only time for a meeting had to be
_____ right after school on Friday.
_____ before school on Monday morning.
_____ at lunch time in the school cafeteria.

Edna and Bill were surprised at the lunch meeting when
_____ no one showed up.
_____ eighty-three students.
_____ the school band showed up.

Name_____ Date_____

┌─ **KEY WORDS** ─────────────────────────────────────┐

| buses | strong | bedrock | build |
| diverted | dam | safe | site |

└──┘

The Large Dam

The state decided to _____ a new dam outside of Centerville.

The old dam, the state said, was no longer _____ . Mr. Wells decided to

take his class to see the _____ of the new and much larger _____ .

The history class from Centerville High School went up into the mountains in

three school _____ . When they got to the new site, the boss for

the construction company explained what had to be done to make the new

dam a _____ and safe one. The first thing, he said, was that Wild

River had to be _____ until his men could dig down deep to

_____ . When finished, he said it would be a wonderful dam.

The state decided to

_____ build a new power plant outside of Centerville.

_____ tear down the old hotel near the center of town.

_____ build a new dam outside of Centerville.

Mr. Wells wanted to take the history classes from Centerville High School to

_____ help build the new dam.

_____ watch the men work on the new dam.

_____ see the site for the new dam.

The boss of the job said that the first thing his men had to do was to

_____ divert Wild River.

_____ plant a lot of trees to hold in the soil.

_____ see if there was oil in the ground.

Name_____ Date_____

The Newspaper Route

Kevin wanted to earn some _____ with a regular job. He told Brian that it did not matter whether it was an inside or an outside _____ . Brian said that the _____ company needed high school students who could drive. He said that the company wanted to have men who would drop newspapers off for students who would then _____ them. Kevin thought that this sounded like a good idea. When he went to the company, the head man told Kevin that he did not look _____ enough. That made Kevin _____ . He told the head man that even though he was _____ , he could lift anything anyone could. The man liked that. He hired Kevin then and _____ .

Kevin told Brian that

_____ he had been very sick.

_____ his car was broken down.

_____ he wanted a job.

Brian told Kevin that

_____ the book store needed someone to work at night.

_____ the newspaper was looking for students who could drive.

_____ he was too short to get a good job.

Kevin got a job with the newspaper because he showed the head man

_____ that he was able to do a good job.

_____ that he was a good cook after all.

_____ that he once worked as a clown for the circus.

Name_____ Date_____

KEY WORDS

wondered	meet	club	free
fair	homes	said	idea

The Club

Barbara and Sue thought it would be a good idea to start a girls' club that could _____ at the high school. They talked to Ellen and Jermaine about it. They both liked the _____ . But when they spoke with Mrs. Bates, the school counselor, she did not like the idea. The girls _____ why. Mrs. Bates _____ that any club that used the high school had to be open to all students. She said that the _____ Barbara and Sue wanted to start would not be open to all students. That would not be _____ , she said. This upset the girls. But Mrs. Bates said that they were _____ to start their club outside of school and meet in their _____ .

Barbara and Sue wanted to

_____ go shopping with Ellen and Jermaine.

_____ start a club at the high school.

_____ start a swimming team.

Ellen and Jermaine thought the idea of a club

_____ was stupid.

_____ was a good idea.

_____ did not interest them at all.

Mrs. Bates said the club could not meet at the school because

_____ it was not open to all students.

_____ the school was not a club house.

_____ she would not be allowed to join it.

Name_____ Date_____

Hot Dog Sale

All the students at Lincoln High School saw the notice on the bulletin _____ . It said there was going to be a hot dog _____ next Monday. The money the school made on the sale would be _____ to feed the poor. Scott and Greg _____ this was a great idea and offered to help. Mr. Lyons, the boys counselor at Lincoln, told Scott and Greg that he liked their interest in what the school was doing. He told them to report to the school _____ on Monday at about 11:30. Then Greg asked what they would be doing. Mr. Lyons said that the best _____ they could give would be to get the hot dogs ready to be _____ . And, he added, if they could _____ anyone else, that would be great.

The notice on the school bulletin board said there would be
_____ no classes on Monday.
_____ a play by the drama department in the school auditorium.
_____ a hot dog sale.

Greg and Scott decided that they would
_____ like to help out at the sale.
_____ skip school on that day.
_____ sell hamburgers at the hot dog sale.

Mr. Lyons told Scott and Greg to
_____ stay away from the sale.
_____ bring others to help.
_____ dress up in their best clothes.

Name_____ Date_____

┌─ **KEY WORDS** ─────────────────────────────────────┐

| dangerous | protect | need | factories |
| long | laws | school | safe |

└──┘

Safety at the Factory

One hundred years ago, factories were often not _____ places for their workers. Quite often children and women worked _____ hours and earned very little. Workers were crowded around machinery that could be _____ and could injure the workers. Because our government wanted children to go to _____ to learn to read and write, laws were created to protect the workers. Now there are many laws that _____ people who work in factories. Some people say that we need more _____ . They say that there are still many _____ that are not completely safe. Someday we will have the laws we _____ to protect everyone who works.

One hundred years ago, factories were often not
  _____ protected from wind and rain and snow.
  _____ safe places for the workers.
  _____ busy all year long.

People who worked in factories a long time ago included
  _____ women and children.
  _____ police dogs to protect the workers.
  _____ college professors.

Some people say that we still do not have
  _____ good machinery in factories.
  _____ enough telephones for everyone to use.
  _____ enough laws to provide the safety people need.

Name_____ Date_____

```
┌─ KEY WORDS ──────────────────────────────────────────────┐
│      staff          roof          torn          hurt       │
│    teachers        classes      problem       condition    │
└────────────────────────────────────────────────────────────┘
```

The School Gym

When the teachers at Roosevelt High School met, they knew there was a
_____ . Mrs. Moore, the school principal, had told them to be
ready for one. Everyone was quiet in the school _____ room. Mrs.
Moore then told all the _____ that the school gym was not in
good _____ . The problem, she said, was that water had
been leaking in for many years. The result was that the _____ was ready
to fall through the building. The safety inspectors had told her that the gym
had to be _____ down and rebuilt. And, she added, it had to be done
right away before anyone got _____ . In the meantime, she said, the
school auditorium would have to be used for gym _____ .

The problem Mrs. Moore told the school staff about was that
        _____ a fire had ruined the school gym.
        _____ the roof on the gym was in bad condition.
        _____ the school would no longer have a football team.

The gym roof was in bad condition because it had been
        _____ on fire last spring.
        _____ leaking for a long time.
        _____ poorly built in the first place.

Mrs. Moore told the teachers that while the gym was being rebuilt they
        _____ would stop all gym classes.
        _____ would have only swimming.
        _____ would use the school auditorium.

Name_____ Date_____

The School Basketball Game

Everyone at Truman High School was excited. Truman High's basketball team was going to play _____ Jefferson High's team. It was the end of the _____ , and these were the two best teams in the _____ . And the game was going to be _____ at Truman High. The school cheer leaders were busy _____ , and the team was working hard on all of its plays. Then it_____ . Lucky Davis, the star player, broke his leg. Could the team _____ without him? Everyone was scared. At first, everyone thought Truman High could whip Jefferson. Now everyone wondered if Jefferson was going to _____ Truman. Now it was a toss up.

Everyone at Truman High was excited because the school basketball team
_____ was going to play Roosevelt High's team.
_____ all had broken out with measles.
_____ was ready to play Jefferson High's team.

The winner of this game would become the
_____ top team in the league.
_____ bottom team in the league.
_____ none of the above.

When Lucky Davis broke his leg, everyone
_____ was excited.
_____ felt Truman might lose the game.
_____ all of the above

Name_____ Date_____

| salary | graduate | enter | members |
| volunteer | idea | students | service |

Community Service

A lot of high schools are now requiring that students, in order to graduate, do up to 100 hours of community _____ . Students should _____ , for example, at a hospital, a church, or a park, and work for no _____ or pay. They must do something that is a help to other people in the community. Whether students are going on to college or are going to work after they _____ from high school, this is an excellent plan. There is almost no end to the kinds of things _____ can volunteer for, and they can start right when they _____ high school. The _____ behind community service is that we are all _____ of the community and should help it.

A lot of high schools are now requiring students to
_____ help clean up the school yard if they miss school a lot.
_____ volunteer in the community for services that help others.
_____ make money by working parttime for hospitals.

Community service is required for students who
_____ are not going to attend college.
_____ are going to attend college.
_____ all students.
_____ none of the above

Community service starts when students
_____ enter high school.
_____ are seniors.
_____ when they graduate from high school.

Name_____ Date_____

```
┌─ KEY WORDS ─────────────────────────────────────────────┐
│       write        properly       dictionary       reader        │
│       tests        ability        against          speller       │
└─────────────────────────────────────────────────────────┘
```

The Spelling Bee

Are you a good _____ ? How have you done on regular spelling _____ and written papers? If you are a good speller, can you spell orally as well as you can when you _____ the words? Maybe you should try out for your school spelling bee and match your ability _____ other good spellers. Some people say that you can practice for a spelling bee (or spelling contest) by studying the _____ . Other people say that going through the dictionary will help, but only a little bit. They say that you must have a "spelling_____" in order to really spell well. Another group of people feel that you will be a good speller if you know that a word is not _____ spelled when you see it written. And, they say, if you are a good _____ , you will probably be a good reader.

Good spellers seem to be able to write words as correctly as
_____ when they spell them orally.
_____ when they take spelling tests.
_____ when they are under pressure.

Using a dictionary to prepare for a spelling bee
_____ won't be any help.
_____ should be some help.
_____ is the very best way to prepare for a spelling bee.

If you are a good speller, you probably are a good
_____ cook.
_____ bicycle rider.
_____ reader.

Name_____ Date_____

The Goldfish Bowl

Mrs. Williams thought that her fourth _____ class would like a fish bowl in the classroom. So she bought a bowl that held two gallons of _____ and two pretty little _____ . She bought some gravel and a few fake _____ . The fish bowl looked just beautiful when it was filled with water. The children in the fourth grade liked _____ the fish. But even though they were _____ every day, the goldfish died after a month. The children knew what was _____ . Can you guess what Mrs. Williams _____ to do?

Mrs. Williams got the fish for her classroom because
_____ she knew the children did not like watching fish.
_____ she knew the children would enjoy having the fish in the room.
_____ none of the above

Mrs. Williams probably put fake plants in the fish bowl because
_____ the fish would eat them.
_____ the fish could hide in them.
_____ they looked pretty.

The thing that Mrs. Williams forgot was to
_____ feed the fish every day.
_____ watch them swim around the bowl everyday.
_____ change the water regularly so the fish got oxygen.

Name_____ Date_____

┌─ KEY WORDS ──────────────────────────────┐

small   volunteers   moved   school

surprised   years   floor   many

└──┘

Helping Out at the School Library

Mr. Wright, the school librarian, was swamped with work. The library was too _____ and there were too _____ books. The result was that books were not properly filed and ended up in stacks on the _____ . After asking for more space for what seemed like years, the school board finally gave Mr. Wright an additional two rooms. The school nurse's office was moved across to the high _____ . And that's the space Mr. Wright was given. Mrs. Carlson, the principal at Andrew Jackson High, asked for _____ who could help Mr. Wright. A lot of books had to be _____ . She thought there would be at least fifty volunteers. Everyone was _____ when only three students signed up. Everyone forgot that it was football season!

Mr. Wright had problems. His library was

_____ too big.

_____ too tall.

_____ too small.

And Mr. Wright had

_____ lots of first aid materials stored in the library.

_____ lots of nurse materials stored in the library.

_____ lots of books with nowhere to put them.

When Mr. Wright was given two additional rooms,

_____ more than fifty students signed up to help him.

_____ twelve teachers signed up to help him.

_____ three students signed up to help him .

Name_____ Date_____

┌─ **KEY WORDS** ──┐

      develops   point   chess   right

      class   asked   king   practice

└──┘

All About Chess

"What we need at this high school is a chess club," Jim said to Wally as they were leaving the gym after football _____ . Wally just looked at Jim. He thought to himself, "Who plays chess anyway?" As they walked back to _____ , Jim kept on talking about the skills a person needs to play _____ . And, he said, the skills the game _____ .

    "That's the game with all those pieces, isn't it?" Wally _____ .

    "That's _____ ! The rooks, the pawns, the knights, the bishops, the king, and the queen," Jim answered.

    "I just don't see the point of it," Wally said.

    "The _____ is to checkmate or corner the _____ ."

    "Sounds easy to me," Wally said.

Jim just smiled at his buddy.

        Jim was trying to tell Wally how exciting it was to

            _____ practice football every day at school.

            _____ play checkers with chess pieces.

            _____ play chess.

        "The point of chess is to," Jim said,

            _____ "capture the queen."

            _____ "checkmate the king."

            _____ none of the above

      What do you think?

            _____ Wally thought chess was easy.

            _____ Wally thought chess was hard.

            _____ Wally had played chess for many years.

Name_____ Date_____

┌─ KEY WORDS ──────────────────────────────────┐

| screaming | annoyed | students | delighted |
| trying | drills | lives | important |

└──┘

The Fire Drill

Schools across the country are required to have fire _____ at regular intervals. The purpose of these drills is to see that teachers and _____ know how to move safely from the building. If students start running or _____ , not only will they get hurt but others will as well. It is also _____ that the students know which way to leave their classroom. If too many students are _____ to leave by the same exit, it can cause pushing and shoving that can hurt other students and teachers. Sometimes students get _____ that there is what seems like too many fire drills. Sometimes they are _____ that they are missing a class. What they should be pleased with is that what they are doing could save their _____ .

Schools are required to have
_____ regular picnics every four weeks.
_____ regular fire drills.
_____ regular first aid drills.

One of the purposes of regular fire drills is to train students
_____ how to safely get to the school cafeteria on time.
_____ how to leave school each day.
_____ how to handle themselves in a real fire.

What students should be pleased with in a fire drill is that
_____ it helps the fire department in the town.
_____ it helps the teachers at the school.
_____ it could save their lives.

Name_____ Date_____

After School Job

Television station YMGO asked the principal of Cleveland High _____ , Mrs. Waters, if they could film a TV _____ at the high school about first aid. An article about Cleveland High's first aid program had been written about in the Sentinel, the town _____ , by Ross Harris. Now Ross wanted to come to the school and show more people how good the program was. _____ were asked to be at the first _____ room on Wednesday, 11:00 a.m. The regular first aid _____ had 18 students in it. On Wednesday, _____ 90 students showed up. The _____ that Ross faced was what to do with so many students for what was supposed to be a small class.

The local television station wanted to film a show at the high school

_____ about the number of fights going on every day.

_____ on the food training program.

_____ about the first aid program.

Ross Harris had gotten people interested in the first aid program when he

_____ made a TV film about the program.

_____ was badly hurt and saved by several students.

_____ wrote a story about it for the Sentinel.

When Wednesday arrived, Ross was surprised that

_____ the first aid room was locked.

_____ nearly 90 students showed up.

_____ only 18 students showed up.

Name_____ Date_____

The School Newspaper

Sara Martin was so excited when she became editor of the school
_____ . It was a big job and she knew it would take time
after _____ and on _____ . But she had been
on the staff of the newspaper since she had been a _____
and felt she could do a good job. The first thing that she and Mr. Wright did
was to meet and work out a _____ . They had to figure out
how to have the newspaper out, on time, every _____ weeks. But Sara
was lucky. She had twenty-two people on the newspaper _____
to help get the job _____ .

Sara was happy because she was
_____ the new editor for the school newspaper.
_____ going to write a column for the school newspaper.
_____ going to interview teachers for the school newspaper.

Sara felt she could do a good job because she
_____ was an excellent typist.
_____ knew how to cook quite well.
_____ had been with the newspaper for three years.

Sara was lucky.
_____ She had no staff to help her.
_____ She and Mr. Wright could put the paper out by themselves.
_____ She had twenty-two students on the newspaper staff.

Name_____ Date_____

The Machine Shop

Bert was a good mechanic. Mr. Topps, the teacher in the school machine _____, knew that. In fact, when a _____ job came up, Mr. Topps always asked Bert to _____ it. When new students started in the class, Mr. Topps always asked _____ to get them started. One day, Mr. Topps drove his car to class. He had been having _____ problems. Even he could not figure out what the _____ was. He called Bert over to take a look. Bert opened the _____ and looked inside. He did not say much. Then he removed the carburetor. He looked it over and said, "Mr. Topps, I'm surprised. This carburetor is a _____ of junk! Get a new one." Everyone laughed. Even Mr. Topps!

True or False? (Use a "T" or an "F")

_____ Mr. Topps was the school math teacher.
_____ Bert was the best student in the machine shop class.
_____ Everyone said that Bert could fix anything.
_____ Bert liked to fix typewriters that were broken.
_____ One day Mr. Topps brought his own car to class.
_____ The car was running just fine.
_____ Mr. Topps was having problems with his own car.
_____ Bert took three days to go over Mr. Topps' car.
_____ After looking at the engine, Bert said the fuel pump was a mess.
_____ Bert figured out that Mr. Topps' carburetor was a piece of junk.

Name_____ Date_____

Football Practice

Phil and Frank were happy. They made it on the school football _____ . But could they make it to all the practice sessions? Coach Henderson meant it when he said that missing even one _____ meant you were off the team. He told all the football players that practice was _____ . They had to be at each session because they had to learn all the _____ . Hank got careless. He was not learning all the _____ . Coach Henderson was watching both _____ and Hank. Why was Phil doing so _____ and why was Hank doing so poorly? There was only one thing to do. And that was to take Hank _____ the team.

Phil and Hank were happy because they made it on the
    _____ school soccer team.
    _____ school hockey team.
    _____ school football team.

Coach Henderson wanted all players at all practice sessions so they could
    _____ get to know one another.
    _____ learn all the new plays.
    _____ practice tossing the football to each other.

Hank thought he knew it all. Coach Henderson had to
    _____ throw him off the team.
    _____ make him the team captain.
    _____ give him a new uniform.

Name_____ Date_____

The School Yearbook

Everyone was _____ . A photographer was going to be at Colonial High School on Wednesday. It was picture day. The _____ was going to take pictures of students. Then he was going to walk around the school _____ and take pictures of things going on at the school. He was supposed to be there for _____ days. Mr. Wright, the high school principal, said that hundreds of _____ would be taken. Then the school yearbook _____ would have to select the ones they felt would be best for the yearbook. And, Mr. Wright added, they would have only two _____ to make their selections. That would be not only a big _____ but an important one.

Everyone at Colonial High was excited because
_____ the big football game was going to be played.
_____ the photographer would be there to take pictures.
_____ the school yearbook was being delivered to the school.

After taking pictures of the students, the photographer would
_____ photograph sports events.
_____ photograph things going on at the school.
_____ photograph the school staff.

The yearbook was a big job. The committee would have only
_____ two weeks to make their selections of photographs.
_____ two days to make their selections of photographs.
_____ two months to make their selections of photographs.

Name_____ Date_____

The Championship

Johnson High School finally won the state _____ in basketball. The students and the _____ were excited. In fact, everyone in Grizzly Falls was excited. The mayor _____ that when the team returned home, there would be a holiday in town. All the schools, banks, and stores were going to close. And there would be a parade down Main Street. This was the first championship that the school had won in fifty _____ ! The team had come close a few times but it had never beaten another _____ in the final playoffs. The school band _____ and all the _____ were cleaned and pressed. When the team did return, all tired out, there was a wonderful _____ for them.

Everyone at school and in town was excited because
_____ the fire in town had been put out.
_____ the school basketball team won the local championship.
_____ the school basketball team won the state championship.

The mayor announced that when the team returned
_____ there would be a big party for the team.
_____ there would be a big parade for the team.
_____ there would be a barbeque at school for the team.

Even the school band practiced and
_____ cleaned their instruments.
_____ improved their marching.
_____ cleaned their uniforms.

Name_____ Date_____

The School Grounds

When the school officers met in September, the students said that the school grounds looked _____ . Everyone wondered why, at a brand new high school, no one had planted any _____ . Mrs. Higgins, the school principal, said that trees did _____ important things. The roots held soil from washing _____ . The trees could act as a wind _____ . Trees also, she said, added _____ to any place they were planted. But there was no budget for buying probably 200 trees that would be needed. You guessed it. The _____ said they would _____ the money to buy the trees and then they would plant and care for them.

The school council, at its first meeting, felt the school grounds
_____ looked beautiful.
_____ looked terrible.
_____ looked charming.

Mrs. Higgins said that trees did things like
_____ hold the soil.
_____ form a wind break.
_____ add beauty.
_____ all of these

The students said they would
_____ raise money but not plant or care for the trees.
_____ not raise money but care for and plant the trees.
_____ raise money, plant, and care for the trees.

Name _____ Date _____

┌─ **KEY WORDS** ──┐
| help   apples   announced   Saturday   offered |
| firemen   June   principal   Picnic   swimming |
└──┘

The Senior Barbecue

It was April. It would soon be _____ , the time for the annual Senior _____ and Barbecue. Carlos and Bill asked if they could _____ get it organized. Mr. Grill, the school _____ , told them to go ahead and start planning the Barbecue for the second _____ in June. Carlos and Bill picked a nice spot at Freeman Park just outside of town. It had picnic tables and barbecue pits. It also had a nice, clean _____ pool. As soon as they _____ the day and date to their classmates, everyone _____ to help make it the best senior picnic Mountain High School had ever had.

The seniors at Mountain High School were getting ready for the
   _____ annual school play.
   _____ annual School Picnic and Barbecue.
   _____ last basketball game.

The school principal was
   _____ Mr. James.
   _____ Mr. Wright.
   _____ Mr. Grill.

A nice thing about Freeman Park was that it had
   _____ tennis courts.
   _____ a swimming pool.
   _____ nice green lawns.

Bill and Carlos offered to
   _____ help organize the Picnic.
   _____ decorate the school gym.
   _____ write a school play.

The Annual Senior Picnic and Barbecue would be held at
   _____ the school on a Saturday.
   _____ Sally Myers' house.
   _____ Freeman Park.

The seniors at the high school wanted to make this picnic
   _____ the best they ever had
   _____ a lot of fun for the girls.
   _____ the first ever held at Mountain High School.

Name_____ Date_____

┌─ KEY WORDS ──────────────────────────────────┐
│   roses   said   trombones   instruments   board   │
│   jazz   band   School   redwood   audition │
└──┘

The School Band

Mr. Kelly, the school music teacher at Morse High _____ , announced that the school was going to start a _____ band. Eddy and Tim both played _____ and wanted to be a part of the new _____ . They both signed up to meet Mr. Kelly and to _____ for the band. When they got to the audition, there were thirty other students with their _____ waiting to try out. Eddy turned to Tim and _____ , "This isn't going to be easy. Everyone here is good." The next day Mr. Kelly put a notice on his bulletin _____ . It said: "Everyone who tried out for the new jazz band is accepted. You were all terrific." Eddy and Tim were happy.

Mr. Kelly announced that he was starting

_____ a hunting club.
_____ a jazz band.
_____ a music club.

Eddy and Tim signed up to audition for the

_____ band.
_____ town orchestra.
_____ hunting club.

A better title might be

_____ The Jazz Band
_____ Rock Around the Clock
_____ The School Rock Band

Eddy and Tim both played

_____ the trombone.
_____ the violin.
_____ jazz piano.

When Eddy saw all the students waiting to audition, he felt

_____ it would be a snap.
_____ it wouldn't be easy.
_____ they should leave.

Mr. Kelly accepted for the Band

_____ all the boys
_____ all the girls
_____ all who auditioned

Name_____ Date_____

Home Economics

Carla and Bertie both knew how to cook a few _____ . But they wanted to learn how to be _____ in the kitchen! The answer? They decided to take the school course in _____ economics. That was the cooking course at Monroe High _____ . When they started the course, they realized that it was going to cover more than _____ . But that was all right with them. It really covered how to manage a home. Mrs. Carson showed the class _____ how to study contracts for purchasing appliances, how to properly operate stoves, refrigerators, and washing machines, and even how to answer the _____ ! They even discussed baby care. After one month, Carla turned to Bertie and said, "Enough is _____ . When do we start learning how to cook?"

Carla and Bertie
    _____ were excellent cooks.
    _____ knew how to cook a few
        dishes.
    _____ wanted to know how to
        repair dishwashers.

The teacher for the class was
    _____ Mr. Monroe.
    _____ Ms. Carlson.
    _____ Mrs. Carson.

After a month, Carla wondered when
    _____ Bertie would teach the
        course.
    _____ Mrs. Carson would show
        them how to cook.
    _____ Mr. Monroe would come
        to class.

The girls decided to take the
    _____ home economics class.
    _____ machine shop so that
        they could repair things.
    _____ sewing class because they
        wanted to make dresses

The girls were surprised when the course included
    _____ signing contracts.
    _____ answering telephones.
    _____ operating stoves.
    _____ all of the above

What would you call this story if you had to give it a name?

_____

Name_____ Date_____

valuable	at	echo	food	students
placed	sewing	cafeteria	said	lunches

Lunch Time in the Cafeteria

A large sign was made by the principal's office at Tree Haven High School. It was _____ at the door to the school cafeteria. Here is what it _____ . "There has been too much noise _____ lunch time in the school _____ . We are asking all _____ who buy their _____ to be quieter when they eat. The cafeteria has a very bad _____ . We will all be better off by not yelling so much as we get our _____ and eat it."

The principal's office made a large
_____ bowl of soup.
_____ sign.
_____ chocolate cake.

The sign said the school cafeteria was too noisy during
_____ basketball games.
_____ school dances.
_____ lunch time.

What do you think happened:
_____ the students made more noise
_____ the students did not care
_____ the students cooperated

The sign was put
_____ on the school bulletin board.
_____ in the boys' gym.
_____ on the door to the school cafeteria.

The reason for the sign was that there were too many
_____ echoes.
_____ students.
_____ teachers.

Can you think of a better title for this story?

_____

Name_____ Date_____

KEY WORDS

difficult	Saturday	Forget	carnation	stopping
hike	afternoon	alibi	good	house

Mountain Hike

The weather was so _____ , Mel turned to Jeff after algebra class and said, "Come on, Jeff. How about taking a _____ with me up to Spring Mountain on Saturday."

"Sounds all right to me. We'll meet at 8:30 at my _____ ," Jeff said.

That _____ , at 8:30, Mel was on time to meet Jeff. They both wore comfortable clothing. And since it would be a warm day, they had their hiking shorts on and their hiking boots.

They knew from hiking up Spring Mountain before that it was about a 6 mile hike. And in some places it could be _____ because there were no paths. But everyone knew that a good _____ place halfway up the mountain slope was Hiker's Fountain, a natural spring that was a place to rest.

When they got back that _____ to Jeff's house, Mel said, "Well, are you ready to go again tomorrow?"

"_____ it," Jeff said.

Jeff wanted to go on a hike with
_____ Carla.
_____ Bert.
_____ Mel.

The hike was to be up the slopes of
_____ Mt. Whitby.
_____ Winter Mountain.
_____ Spring Mountain.

Mel and Jeff decided to meet on
_____ Saturday at 8:30.
_____ Sunday at 10:30.
_____ Wednesday at 5:00.

They decided to meet at
_____ Hiker's Rest.
_____ Hiker's Fountain.
_____ Jeff's house.

Hiker's Fountain was
_____ near the top of the
mountain.
_____ near the bottom.
_____ halfway to the top.

When they got back, Jeff was
_____ happy.
_____ tired.
_____ sick.

Name_____ Date_____

KEY WORDS

strand	ready	raining	support	win
set	runners	teaspoon	Wilson	meet

The Track Team

The track team at Carver High School was all _____ to have its first _____ against Wilson High on Saturday. Everyone at school was excited. Coach Weaver had worked the team hard but felt they were _____ to win. Carver had never won a meet when running against _____ . Jim, Sam, and Marty, the star _____ , were in topnotch condition. Coach Weaver felt confident. In fact, the whole team felt they were ready to _____ their first meet against Wilson and the first meet of the season. Everyone was giving Jim, Sam, and Marty all kinds of _____ . Even the teachers at Carver were in back of the team. But you can imagine how everyone felt on Saturday when it was _____ . The meet had to be cancelled! Mr. Edwards felt it was too dangerous to run in such a downpour.

The track team at Carver was
_____ not ready for the meet.
_____ ready for the meet.
_____ going to have a picnic.

Coach Weaver felt that Carver
_____ would easily win.
_____ might win by a margin.
_____ would probably lose.

Even the teachers supported
_____ the runners.
_____ the basketball team.
_____ the baseball team.

Carver was scheduled to run against
_____ Weaver High School.
_____ Edwards High School.
_____ Wilson High School.

The three top stars on the team were
_____ Jim, Sam, and Eddy.
_____ Jim, Sam, and Marty.
_____ Marty, Mr. Edwards, and Coach Weaver.

But because of bad weather, the meet
_____ was held anyway.
_____ was cancelled.
_____ was delayed till evening.

Name_____ Date_____

The Car Wash

Casey looked over at Hal and said, "You know what? The senior _____ is coming up in four months, and the _____ class doesn't have more than $40 to get it going."

"I've been thinking about that, too," Hal answered. "And I've been thinking that we could raise some money by having a series of car _____ . Let's get our friends together and meet on _____ in the school gym at 3:30."

That Monday, when _____ was together Bill and Steve _____ they ask Mr. Carter, the school principal, if they could use the school _____ for the car washes. Mrs. Wilson, the school secretary, said she thought it would be all right.

"Fine. Then let's get an announcement out that we'll have the first car wash next Saturday. And all _____ will have to help," Bill said.

Casey said the senior class
_____ was lazy.
_____ should have a dance.
_____ had only $40.

To get the idea going, the seniors
_____ went to see Mr. Carter.
_____ had a meeting.
_____ picketed the school.

Mr. Carter could not attend the meeting, but
_____ Bertie and Jayne were there.
_____ Mrs. Carter attended.
_____ his secretary, Mrs. Wilson, was there.

The idea for a car wash came from
_____ Mrs. Wilson.
_____ Hal.
_____ Casey.

The first car wash was scheduled for
_____ Wednesday.
_____ Monday.
_____ Saturday.

Why do you think the seniors wanted to raise money?
_____ to split amongst them
_____ to hire a band
_____ to pay for beginning expenses

Name_____ Date_____

Flight Into Space

Most of the students at Roosevelt High School were lined up. The space ship was _____ passengers. The students with correct _____ passes were entering the ship. There was a great deal of _____ .

Jeanie called out to Sara, "I wish you were going on this trip. I think it is going to be _____ ." Sara did not say anything. She just watched as the _____ climbed on board.

Sara watched as _____ of her friends disappeared on to the space ship.

Then a voice called out: "We are now loaded. We will be departing in ten minutes. Please _____ back from the rockets."

Sara knew that this was an experimental trip. She knew that the Aquarius was an experiment. But she was not ready to be part of an experiment in space to help find life in other _____ .

Jeanie was boarding the
_____ airplane.
_____ train.
_____ space ship.

Sara
_____ wanted to be with Jeanie.
_____ did not have a boarding pass.
_____ was not ready for the trip.

Jeanie was to be part of a trip to
_____ Mars.
_____ Capricorn.
_____ other worlds.

The voice called out that the space ship would leave
_____ from Wilson High School.
_____ from Washington, D.C.
_____ in ten minutes.

This trip into space was
_____ an accident.
_____ all for fun.
_____ an experiment.

The name of the space ship was the
_____ Challenger.
_____ Explorer.
_____ Aquarius.

Name_____ Date_____

┌─ KEY WORDS ───┐

issue   allowing   groceries   new   members

carton   one   pleased   newspaper   volunteered

└──┘

The School Newspaper

Mrs. Leone looked over journalism class. It looked like a good group. She was _____ that the school board was _____ the students to publish two issues a month of the school _____ . Last year, they were allowed to publish only _____ issue a month.

Maria and Teresa _____ to write about school activities. Carlos said he would handle sports. Julio said that he would do interviews on faculty _____ . And Carlos said he would like to write on general school news.

Mrs. Leone was happy. This was a whole _____ group of students. She was not even sure how well they could write. But the first _____ of the new school year had to be out in three weeks. She felt they could make their goal.

The teacher in charge of the newspaper was
_____ Mr. Wilson.
_____ Mr. Carter.
_____ Mrs. Leone.

This year the school was permitting two issues
_____ a year.
_____ a week.
_____ a month.

Maria and Teresa offered to write about
_____ school health problems.
_____ movies.
_____ school news.

Carlos offered to write the news about
_____ sports.
_____ school safety.
_____ school traffic.

Mrs. Leone was
_____ disappointed.
_____ happy.
_____ saddened.

Mrs. Leone felt the students
_____ would make their goal.
_____ do a bad job.
_____ would not work hard.

Name_____ Date_____

The Siren

There was a loud _____ . Everyone was winning the _____ game against Petersen High by 9-8. And there was Mike Plant rolling around on the _____ . The game stopped and McKinley's coach. Ed Wright called for time out.

Sam Edwards, _____ of the team, was kneeling next to Mike. Then someone announced over the loudspeaker, "Call an _____ . Mike Plant has a broken leg." Four students came running out on the field with a stretcher and carefully loaded Mike on to it. Then they trotted off the field.

Within minutes, there was the sound of a _____ . The ambulance from City _____ pulled on to the playing field. Mike was loaded in and it immediately drove off. The crowd gave Mike a loud round of _____ . Then the game went on with McKinley winning.

The game stopped at McKinley when
_____ the spectators heard a
    scream.
_____ Petersen scored a goal.
_____ Coach Edwards broke his
    leg.

When Sam saw Mike on the ground he
_____ fainted.
_____ knelt beside him.
_____ called for the coach.

When the ambulance took off
_____ Mike was not in it.
_____ the spectators applauded.
_____ Coach Wright stopped the
    game.

During the soccer game
_____ it started to rain.
_____ Sam hurt himself.
_____ Mike Plant broke his leg.

Four students ran out on the field
_____ with Mrs. Decker, the
    school nurse.
_____ with Dr. Brody.
_____ with a strecther.

When the game ended, the winning team was
_____ Wilson High.
_____ Roosevelt High.
_____ Petersen High.

Name_____ Date_____

The Garage Sale

Sally and Barbara heard that Rick and Pablo were going to have a _____
sale to raise money for the _____ class at West Side High. They decided
that they would give their two friends a _____ hand. Rick and Pablo
were pleased. They knew it would take _____ than just the two of them to do
it right. They decided that they would put up _____ announcing the
sale to be held in one month on a Saturday. Sally and Barbara offered to make the
posters and put them around the _____ . Bob, the class president, liked
the idea. Then they had to round up items for the _____ . They stored
everything in Bob's garage. Everyone _____ things they wanted to get
rid of. The sale was a great success. They raised almost $400!

The sale would be held on a
_____ Sunday.
_____ Saturday.
_____ Tuesday.

The sale was to raise money for the
_____ West Side band.
_____ West Side senior class.
_____ Red Cross.

The class president was
_____ Barbara.
_____ Bob.
_____ Rick.

The posters were made and put up by
_____ Rick and Pablo.
_____ Bob.
_____ Sally and Barbara.

The garage sale items were stored in
_____ Bob's garage.
_____ Sally's barn.
_____ Pablo's patio.

The successful sale raised almost
_____ $400.
_____ $300.
_____ $1000.

Name_____ Date_____

The Surprise

Mr. Wilkins, the music _____ at New Castle High, had everyone in the band sit down after music period. "The school band has been _____ to play at City Park next Sunday," he said. "What an honor," Bill Sanders said. "Yes, it is. We'll play our marching _____ for about an hour," Mr. Wilkins said. One of the students wondered what the band should wear. "That's a good _____ . The new _____ we ordered three months ago will be delivered to you on _____ . Be sure to wear them," Mr. Wilkins said. Sunday arrived and everyone was _____ for Mr. Wilkins at 2:00 p.m. But no one was wearing a uniform. "What happened?" Mr. Wilkins asked. "Why aren't you in uniform?" "The truck broke down. No _____ ," answered Paul. "Never mind," said Mr. Wilkins. "It's not what we're wearing but how the music sounds that counts."

Where was the New Castle High band to play?
_____ at the circus
_____ at a football game
_____ at City Park

When was the New Castle High band to play?
_____ Thanksgiving
_____ Sunday afternoon
_____ Fourth of July

Mr. Wilkins said the band would play
_____ all afternoon.
_____ fifteen minutes.
_____ about an hour.

The uniforms had been ordered
_____ three months ago.
_____ three weeks ago.
_____ six months ago.

Mr. Wilkins arrived at the park at
_____ noon.
_____ midnight.
_____ 2:00 p.m.

The uniforms did not arrive because
_____ the factory caught on fire.
_____ the truck broke down.
_____ they were sent to another school.

Name_____ Date_____

banjo	auditorium	did	offered	model	advertising
class	work	soda	affair	handle	opinion

The Fashion Show

One of the things the tenth grade _____ did every year at Wilson High was to have a fashion show. Bertie and Ginger wanted to put this _____ together. They knew it would take a lot of hard _____ . Molly and Sandra _____ to contact local dress shops. Ted and Jim said they would _____ the lighting in the school _____ . Other class members said they would _____ the dresses. Eddie, Tom, and Sal said they would take care of the _____ so they would get a good crowd. Betty said that she and Carla would see if they could get some dresses donated for door prizes. Mrs. Evans, the tenth grade counselor, was pleased that the class was working so well together.

Every year the fashion show was held by the
_____ senior class.
_____ PTA.
_____ tenth grade class.

Fashions for the show would be donated by
_____ local dress shops.
_____ a department store.
_____ a thrift shop.

The lighting would be handled by
_____ Ted and Jim.
_____ Eddie and Tom.
_____ Molly and Sandra.

The show would be held in the
_____ gymnasium.
_____ cafeteria.
_____ auditorium.

Mrs. Evans was the
_____ tenth grade counselor.
_____ assistant principal.
_____ home economics teacher.

Eddie, Tom, and Sal were in charge of
_____ refreshments.
_____ advertising.
_____ tickets.

Name_____ Date_____

┌─ KEY WORDS ──────────────────────────────────┐
│   apricot   apply   winners   hot rod   people   crowded   │
│   money   help   apple   highway   experience   earn   │
└──┘

The Bingo Game

Tom and Chris wanted to get a job to earn some _____ . All the jobs they found wanted boys with _____ . One day at school, Tom told Chris he had heard that the Community Center needed _____ at their weekly bingo game. It would only be one night a week, but they could _____ $5.00 an hour. When they went to _____ for the job, Mrs. Wright hired them on the spot. She needed two boys to work five hours every Friday night. She told them they would have to pass out bingo cards and help the caller. It all sounded all right to Tom and Chris. They knew that a lot of older folks liked to play bingo once a week and that the place would be _____ . That Friday it rained and rained. When Tom and Chris got to the center, there were only three _____ waiting to play. "Sorry, boys," Mrs. Wright said. "We've had to cancel the games tonight."

The bingo games were held at the
　　_____ high school.
　　_____ Community Center.
　　_____ church.

If Tom and Chris were hired, they would get
　　_____ $15.00 a night.
　　_____ $20.00 a week.
　　_____ $5.00 an hour.

The bingo games were held on
　　_____ Friday nights.
　　_____ Sunday evenings.
　　_____ Saturday afternoons.

The bingo games went on for
　　_____ two and a half hours.
　　_____ five hours.
　　_____ 120 minutes.

Most jobs want people with
　　_____ money.
　　_____ lots of time.
　　_____ experience.

The very first Friday night the bingo game
　　_____ ran overtime.
　　_____ was cancelled.
　　_____ started late.

Name_____ Date_____

KEY WORDS

earthquake	bed	blocks	horse	do-nut	locked
clock	dressed	milk	flunking	class	office

The Mistake

Tom woke up and looked at his _____ . It was 8:30, and it was Monday morning. What had happened? Why didn't the alarm go off? School started at 8:45. And he had to give an oral report to his first period history _____ . He was in a sweat. He jumped out of _____ , got _____ , grabbed a _____ , and ran out of the house. "What's going on?" his mother called. "I can't talk. I'm late," Tom yelled back. McKinley High was eight _____ away. He ran all the way. That's funny, he thought. Where is everyone. Am I that late? He was _____ history. He really needed to give a good report. The school doors were _____ . Then he realized it was a school holiday!

Tom woke up at
_____ ten o'clock.
_____ noon.
_____ 8:30.

School started at
_____ 8:45.
_____ 8:00.
_____ 9:00.

Tom's first period class was
_____ English.
_____ math.
_____ history.

Tom grabbed a
_____ do-nut.
_____ piece of toast.
_____ hard boiled egg.

McKinley High was
_____ two miles from home.
_____ way across town.
_____ eight blocks away.

The school doors were locked because it was
_____ summer vacation.
_____ Christmas.
_____ a school holiday.

Name_____ Date_____

| fire | good | other | fantastic | waiting | twisted |
| match | energy | seven | gym | truck | himself |

The Wrestling Match

The wrestling _____ was set for next Thursday. Everyone at Los Robles High was excited. At last maybe Los Robles could win against Satterfield High, which had not lost a match in _____ years. The star of the team, Jose, was in good condition. He felt he could win against Paul from Satterfield. Jose had not lost a match in three years. He was _____ and he knew it, and so did everyone else at Los Robles. Jose had been _____ for the match. he wanted to win it for _____ and for Los Robles High. The day of the match came. The school _____ was filled with students from both schools. Everyone was shouting. Jose and Paul entered the ring. Then they pounced on each _____ . Jose let out a scream. He had _____ his knee. Somehow he managed to keep on trying to win. Finally Jose pinned Paul down until the referee yelled, "It's a win for Los Robles!" The students went wild. At last they had won against Satterfield!

The wrestling match was between Los Robles and
_____ Satterfield.
_____ Fairview.
_____ Western.

Satterfield High had not lost a match in
_____ four years.
_____ seven years.
_____ ten years.

The star of the Los Robles team was
_____ Paul.
_____ Jose.
_____ Sam.

The match was held on a
_____ Friday.
_____ Thursday.
_____ Saturday.

Jose let out a yell because he hurt his
_____ elbow.
_____ wrist.
_____ knee.

The referee yelled,
_____ "It's a win for Satterfield."
_____ "It's a tie."
_____ "It's a win for Los Robles."

Name_____ Date_____

Jamming It Up

Paul, Eric, and Stan met in the school _____ at lunch. They all played good

_____ . They wanted to form a small combo but they needed a

_____ . Paul suggested they ask Ziggy if he wanted to join with

_____ . They figured they could practice on _____ . Paul

said they could meet at his house and jam. Stan said that Judd might be able to get

them some jobs. It sounded great to all of them. They thought they could play at

school _____ and make a couple of bucks. The first Saturday at Paul's

house they brought their instruments and amps. They sounded great. Everything

went well until Mr. Carlson, Paul's next door neighbor, came over. The noise, he

said, was driving him crazy. The amps were set too _____ . They decided to

call themselves "The Crazies," and they made $50 on their first _____ .

Paul, Eric, and Stan played
  _____ piano.
  _____ guitar.
  _____ trombone.

Ziggy played
  _____ guitar.
  _____ clarinet.
  _____ drums.

The boys planned to practice on
  _____ Saturdays.
  _____ Friday nights.
  _____ Sundays.

The first practice was held at
  _____ Eric's father store.
  _____ Paul's house.
  _____ Stan's aunt's house.

Mr. Carlson said the music was
  _____ just great.
  _____ too loud.
  _____ too long.

On their first job The Crazies made
  _____ $15.00.
  _____ $500.00.
  _____ $50.00.

Name_____ Date_____

KEY WORDS

forgery   experience   period   decided   telephone   easy

office   sailboat   notice   included   entertaining   job

After School Job

Ellie had been getting good grades in her senior year. When she read that the school _____ needed some part-time help, she immediately went to see Mrs. Diggins, the school secretary. Ellie told Mrs. Diggins she had seen the _____ on the school bulletin board and really felt she could come in for an hour a day to help out. Mrs. Diggins explained that there was no pay for the _____ but that it would be good _____ . Then she described the kind of work that Ellie would have to do. It _____ filing, attendance reports, and handling the _____ . There were always, Mrs. Diggins said, four girls helping her each period. It sounded like an enjoyable job. But after the first day, Ellie _____ it wasn't fun at all!

Ellie was a

_____ junior.

_____ senior.

_____ freshman.

The office needed

_____ full-time help.

_____ someone fifteen minutes a day.

_____ part-time help.

The pay for the job was

_____ $2.00 an hour.

_____ $10.00 a day.

_____ some office experience.

Each period Mrs. Diggins was helped by

_____ three boys.

_____ two teachers.

_____ four girls.

Ellie's duties included

_____ making coffee.

_____ filing.

_____ emptying wastebaskets.

Ellie lasted in the job for only

_____ one day.

_____ five minutes.

_____ three weeks.

Name_____ Date_____

The School Art Show

Mr. Wright, the art _____ at Shadowland High, decided it was time to have the annual school art show. He had several really talented art _____ and wanted to show their work. He told the students in all of his art _____ and they were all excited. A date was set in May. Mr. Wright formed committees. He needed _____ in getting paintings and art work up in the school _____ . Roxanne and Crystal offered to help with that job. Mickey and Sal said they would _____ the art room and set up _____ . Sally said she would _____ the town newspaper to get publicity. When the day came for the show, the school was filled with parents, friends, and visitors. Everyone agreed it was a great success!

Mr. Wright was
    _____ a coach.
    _____ a librarian.
    _____ an art teacher.

The art show was held in the
    _____ cafeteria.
    _____ auditorium.
    _____ school halls.

The school art show was held
    _____ once a year.
    _____ every month.
    _____ twice a year.

Publicity was handled by
    _____ Roxanne.
    _____ Crystal.
    _____ Sally.

A date was set in
    _____ April.
    _____ March.
    _____ May.

The art show was
    _____ a failure.
    _____ a success.
    _____ cancelled.

Name_____ Date_____

time	school	decorate	change	empty	could
dress	first	three	building	marvelous	penny

Decorating the School Hall

Jackson High was an old _____ . It was a big_____ with three stories. The halls had display cases that were always _____ . This was because no one wanted to take the _____ to put displays in them. Mrs. Elwood asked her social studies class if they would like to put displays in the empty cases just on the _____ floor. The class agreed. Then she asked them for suggestions on how to _____ the three cases. Bill suggested that one could be about dinosaurs. Betty said she thought one could be on _____ fashions during the 1800s. Eddie thought that one should be about engines. Charlene thought one could show how cave men lived. As soon as the class decided on what they wanted to do, Mrs. Elwood broke the class into _____ groups. Then her students started to work on the three displays.

Jackson High was a big building with
_____ four stories.
_____ five stories.
_____ three stories.

Mrs. Elwood broke the class into
_____ half.
_____ thirds.
_____ quarters.

Mrs. Elwood taught
_____ algebra.
_____ social studies.
_____ Spanish.

Betty wanted one case to display
_____ dinosaurs.
_____ dress fashions.
_____ engines.

The class decided to decorate display cases
_____ just on the first floor.
_____ on all three floors.
_____ in the basement.

Charlene wanted one case to display
_____ how cave men lived.
_____ butterfly collections.
_____ stamp collections.

Name_____ Date_____

A Lucky Meeting

The weather was _____ . I decided I couldn't stay indoors on such a grand day. Since the city _____ was close, I thought it would be a good _____ to spend the afternoon studying. I walked there in ten _____ and sat under a large oak _____ . I looked around. I saw mothers with their _____ and older folks sitting on wooden _____ in the shade.

An old lady with white hair and wearing a dark sweater was sitting nearby. She smiled at _____ and seemed to be inviting me to sit with her and _____ . Since I didn't feel like studying at all, I closed my book and walked over to her and said hello. She smiled at me but didn't _____ anything. Then I said, "It's a beautiful day, isn't it?" I waited a moment for her to_____. Then she said, "Yes, it is _____ ." I asked her if she came to the _____ very often. She told me that when the weather was good, she visited it regularly. Then she asked what I was _____ . I told her it was my math book and that I wasn't very _____ in math. She then told me that she had been an engineer and that math was very important. She asked if I needed any _____ . I told her I sure did. I opened my book to the chapter on calculus and explained where I was confused. In just ten _____ she had explained it so quickly that I finally understood it for the first time. I thanked her and went back to study under the large _____ tree.

The next day at school my teacher was pleased that I _____ the chapter so well. I went back to the park to _____ the old lady, but I never saw her again.

Any wording is acceptable as long as the student is able to demonstrate understanding of the story.

A Lucky Meeting

The weather was _beautiful_ . I decided I couldn't stay indoors on such a grand day. Since the city _park_ was close, I thought it would be a good _idea_ to spend the afternoon there studying. I walked there in ten _minutes_ and sat under a large oak _tree_ . I looked around. I saw mothers with their _babies_ and older folks sitting on wooden _benches_ in the shade.

An old lady with white hair and wearing a dark sweater was sitting nearby. She smiled at _me_ and seemed to be inviting me to sit with her and _talk_ . Since I didn't feel like studying at all, I closed my book and walked over to her and said hello. She smiled at me but didn't _say_ anything. Then I said, "It's a beautiful day, isn't it?" I waited a moment for her to _answer_ . Then she said, "Yes, it is _beautiful_ ." I asked her if she came to the _park_ very often. She told me that when the weather was good, she visited it regularly. Then she asked what I was _studying_ . I told her it was my math book and that I wasn't very _good_ in math. She then told me that she had been an engineer and that math was very important. She asked if I needed any _help_ . I told her I sure did. I opened my book to the chapter on calculus and explained where I was confused. In just ten _minutes_ she had explained it so quickly that I finally understood it for the first time. I thanked her and went back to study under the large _oak_ tree.

The next day at school my teacher was pleased that I _knew_ the chapter so well. I went back to the park to _thank_ the old lady, but I never saw her again.

Name_____ Date_____

The Science Project

Tom's teacher gave an assignment to his science _____ . Mr. Morris told his class that each _____ would have to create a project and then prepare a _____ on it. He allowed the students three months. Tom thought and _____ about the assignment. What project could he create that was within his ability to handle? He thought about studying the human _____ . He thought about a project concerning rocket _____ in space. He thought about experiments with electricity. But no. These would be too _____ .

When he got home that day, he happened to look into his back yard. Then he remembered that his _____ had said she was going to start some tomato plants. Wow! He could use that as his project. He decided that he would start ten tomato plants. he would give no fertilizer to five. The other five he would regularly fertilize. That would be _____ only difference. Then he would count the number of _____ from each plant, pick them, and weigh them. Luckily, his mother had a kitchen scale.

On Saturday he _____ ten small plants at the nearby nursery, turned over the soil, planted, and watered them. He made sure he put up two _____ . One sign said, "No Fertilization." The other said, "Fertilizer." Once a week he put fertilizer around five of the _____ and watered all of the _____ carefully. Soon all the plants were _____ and starting to bloom with little yellow flowers. But where were the _____ ? Then he discovered what was happening. The snails were eating them. The experiment had _____ . "Oh, well," he thought, "I bet Thomas Edison's experiments weren't always successful the first time around!"

Any wording is acceptable as long as the student is able to demonstrate understanding of the story.

The Science Project

Tom's teacher gave an assignment to his science _class_. Mr. Morris told his class that each _student_ would have to create a project and then prepare a _report_ on it. He allowed the students three months. Tom thought and _thought_ about the assignment. What project could he create that was within his ability to handle? He thought about studying the human _body_. He thought about a project concerning rocket _flights_ in space. He thought about experiments with electricity. But no. These would be too _difficult_.

When he got home that day, he happened to look into his back yard. Then he remembered that his _mother_ had said she was going to start some tomato plants. Wow! He could use that as his project. He decided that he would start ten tomato plants. he would give no fertilizer to five. The other five he would regularly fertilize. That would be _the_ only difference. Then he would count the number of _tomatoes_ from each plant, pick them, and weigh them. Luckily, his mother had a kitchen scale.

On Saturday he _bought_ ten small plants at the nearby nursery, turned over the soil, planted, and watered them. He made sure he put up two _signs_. One sign said, "No Fertilization." The other said, "Fertilizer." Once a week he put fertilizer around five of the _plants_ and watered all of the _plants_ carefully. Soon all the plants were _growing_ and starting to bloom with little yellow flowers. But where were the _tomatoes_? Then he discovered what was happening. The snails were eating them. The experiment had _failed_. "Oh, well," he thought, "I bet Thomas Edison's experiments weren't always successful the first time around!"

Name_____ Date_____

The Challenge!

Professor George Wilkins was _____ when the government space program asked _____ to design a _____ platform that would accommodate 200 workers and that could stay out in _____ for two years. Its important mission would be to study the greenhouse _____ as the platform circled the Earth. Not only did Professor Wilkins have to _____ all the technical aspects of the _____ but he had to make sure that recreational facilities were provided in the _____ . This was an _____ job and a big one. He was allowed two years to design the platform. And the government estimated it would take two years to build. Then the government would have to test and train _____ who not only knew their jobs well but who could live in _____ for two years.

As soon as he accepted the assignment, Professor Wilkins started interviewing engineers who could work with him on the _____ . He knew that it would take him at least six months to _____ thirty topnotch men and women who were _____ on all phases of space technology. Then the real work would begin. Plans would need to be drawn up and approved by the _____ . He and his team would have to study metals that could resist the _____ and tear of space. And they would even have to learn about boredom in space. Professor Wilkins knew he had accepted a difficult but challenging assignment. But then he thought, "I wouldn't miss this experience for the world!"

Any wording is acceptable as long as the student is able to demonstrate understanding of the story.

The Challenge!

Professor George Wilkins was _surprised_ when the government space program asked _him_ to design a _space_ platform that would accommodate 200 workers and that could stay out in _space_ for two years. Its important mission would be to study the greenhouse _effect_ as the platform circled the Earth. Not only did Professor Wilkins have to _design_ all the technical aspects of the _platform_ but he had to make sure that recreational facilities were provided in the _design_. This was an _important_ job and a big one. He was allowed two years to design the platform. And the government estimated it would take two years to build. Then the government would have to test and train _applicants_ who not only knew their jobs well but who could live in _space_ for two years.

As soon as he accepted the assignment, Professor Wilkins started interviewing engineers who could work with him on the _project_. He knew that it would take him at least six months to _hire_ thirty topnotch men and women who were _expert_ on all phases of space technology. Then the real work would begin. Plans would need to be drawn up and approved by the _government_. He and his team would have to study metals that could resist the _wear_ and tear of space. And they would even have to learn about boredom in space. Professor Wilkins knew he had accepted a difficult but challenging assignment. But then he thought, "I wouldn't miss this experience for the world!"

Name_____ Date_____

"Extra" Curricular Activity

Right on the _____ page of the morning edition of the Village Times was the story. Cosmos Film Studios was sending a crew to film an important _____ from its new thriller "The Ape Man." The _____ said that the studio would be hiring teenagers for a scene to be filmed in front of Morgan's Drug _____ . The studio needed about twenty students as background for the scene.

In social studies class that day, Linda and Sue _____ Mrs. Edwards, their teacher, about it. Mrs. Edwards said that it had been discussed at that morning's faculty meeting. It seems that Mr. Barnes, the school principal, had been notified a month previously that the studio would _____ extras. There would be no speaking parts, and any student who was interested would have to take a permission slip home and have it signed. Also, only students with good grades would be considered for release for one day of _____ . While the scene would only take a few minutes in the final film, it would, Mrs. Edwards said, probably take all day to film.

The next day practically everyone in the school returned with a signed _____ slip. "We have a problem," Mrs. Edwards said. "More than 500 _____ want to be interviewed by the studio, so Mr. Barnes has had to restrict the number going for the _____ to 10 each from the 9th, 10th, 11th, and 12th grades. Out of that 40 the studio will select the 20 they _____ ." Linda slid down in her chair and whispered to Sue, "Do you think we'll make it?" "Sure," grinned Sue. "By this time next year we'll both probably be stars!"

Any wording is acceptable as long as the student is able to demonstrate understanding of the story.

"Extra" Curricular Activity

Right on the ___*front*___ page of the morning edition of the Village Times was the story. Cosmos Film Studios was sending a crew to film an important ___*scene*___ from its new thriller "The Ape Man." The ___*article*___ said that the studio would be hiring teenagers for a scene to be filmed in front of Morgan's Drug ___*Store*___. The studio needed about twenty students as background for the scene.

In social studies class that day, Linda and Sue ___*asked*___ Mrs. Edwards, their teacher, about it. Mrs. Edwards said that it had been discussed at that morning's faculty meeting. It seems that Mr. Barnes, the school principal, had been notified a month previously that the studio would ___*need*___ extras. There would be no speaking parts, and any student who was interested would have to take a permission slip home and have it signed. Also, only students with good grades would be considered for release for one day of ___*shooting*___. While the scene would only take a few minutes in the final film, it would, Mrs. Edwards said, probably take all day to film.

The next day practically everyone in the school returned with a signed ___*permission*___ slip. "We have a problem," Mrs. Edwards said. "More than 500 ___*students*___ want to be interviewed by the studio, so Mr. Barnes has had to restrict the number going for the ___*interview*___ to 10 each from the 9th, 10th, 11th, and 12th grades. Out of that 40 the studio will select the 20 they ___*need*___." Linda slid down in her chair and whispered to Sue, "Do you think we'll make it?" "Sure," grinned Sue. "By this time next year we'll both probably be stars!"